This book belongs to

The author and publisher are indebted to Diane Melvin,
Senior Clinical Child Psychologist for the
Riverside Health Authority, London, for her invaluable help
in the preparation of this book.

Designed by Alison Fenton

First published in 1989 by Conran Octopus Limited
37 Shelton Street, London WC2H 9HN

© 1989 Conran Octopus Limited

ISBN 1 85029 227 2

Printed in Italy

FIRST EXPERIENCES

Moving House

Barbara Taylor Cork
Illustrated by Siobhan Dodds

Conran Octopus

This is Lucy and her brother, Tom.
Soon they are moving to a new house.

Today, a family has come to look around
their old house.
Mum takes them upstairs to show
them all the bedrooms.

When they have gone, Lucy feels sad and cross.
'I don't want anyone else sleeping in my room,'
she says, grumpily.
'Cheer up,' says Mum. 'In the new house,
you'll have a room of your very own.'

'Would you like to go and see the new house?'
asks Dad. 'We need to talk to the owners.'
'Yes please,' says Lucy, running to the car.
On the way there, they pass a big park.
The playground is full of children.

Lucy and her friend, Sally, are sad to say goodbye.
'Sally can come and visit us in our new house,
very soon,' says Mum.

When they get home, Tom and Dad are busy packing things into big boxes.

Lucy helps Mum sort out her old clothes. 'I never wear these,' says Mum. 'Put them in a pile to give away.'

On moving day, Tom and Lucy wake up early.
The removal men arrive with a big van.

The two removal men, Bill and Fred, help them pack everything into boxes.
Bill wraps the glasses in special paper, so that they won't break during the move.

Bill and Fred carry the heavy furniture and boxes to the van.
When they have finished, the house doesn't look like Tom and Lucy's home any more.

Mum puts Fluff, the cat, into her basket.
She puts her in the car with them.
'Off we go,' says Dad cheerfully.
The children wave goodbye to
their old house.

At the new house, they are very excited.
Their footsteps sound very loud
when they run around the empty rooms.

'Come and have tea before the van arrives,'
says Mum, unpacking the picnic she has made.
They sit on the floor to eat.

Soon Bill and Fred arrive in the van.
Mum tells them where to put everything.

When some of the boxes are unpacked,
the new house begins to feel like home.

Mum and Dad are very tired.
Moving house is hard work.

Tom and Lucy go outside to play.
The garden is much bigger than their old one.
Tom really likes it.

Lucy isn't so happy.
The new house and garden feel strange,
and she misses her friend, Sally.

'Time for bed,' calls Mum. 'You're sharing
a bedroom tonight.'
Lucy is pleased that she is not sleeping on her own.
Perhaps she will tomorrow night.

With their own beds and some of their toys,
the bedroom feels almost like their old room.
'We'll unpack the rest of your things in the morning,'
says Mum, kissing them goodnight.

The next morning, the doorbell rings.
'Is this your cat?' asks a little girl.
'I found her in my garden. I'm Amy.
I live next door.'
'Yes it's Fluff,' says Lucy. 'Thank you.'

Lucy invites Amy to see her new room.
'What a lovely room,' says Amy, 'and look
at all your toys. I'm glad you've come
to live next door.'
'So am I,' says Lucy, smiling at
her new friend.

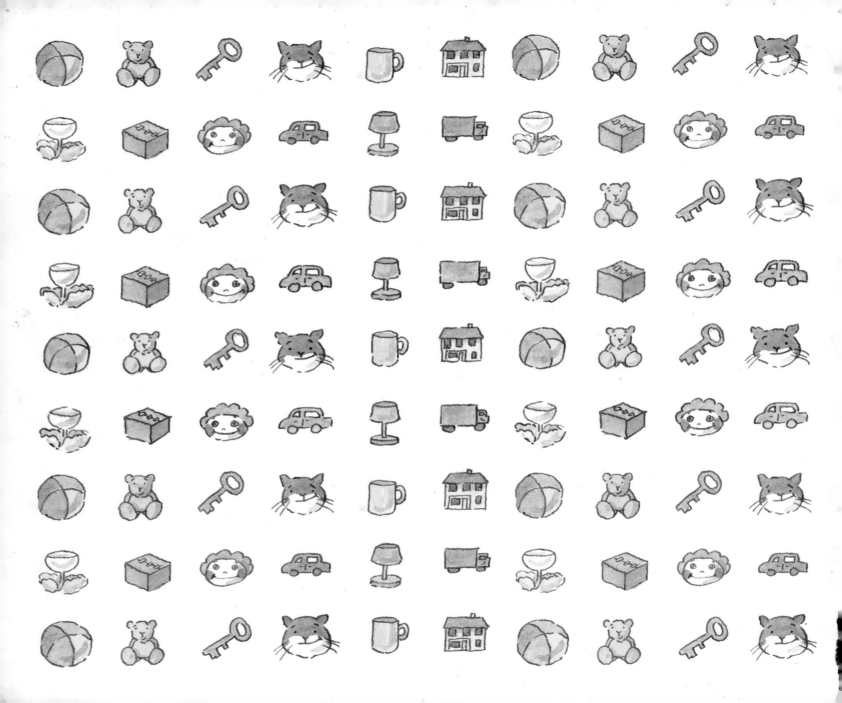